Hansel and Gretel

Penny Dolan and Graham Philpot

W

FRANKLIN WATTS

Hansel and Gretel lived beside a great forest. Their father was a woodcutter and the family were often hungry.

One day, he gave them crusts of bread and sent them into the forest. "Maybe they will find better luck there," he thought.

Gretel was worried. "How will we get back home?"

"I will drop breadcrumbs to mark the path," Hansel told her.

However, while the children searched for blackberries, the birds ate up the breadcrumbs.

Now they were truly lost.

Hansel and Gretel spied a strange cottage hidden in the trees. As they ran closer, they saw it was made of gingerbread and sweets.

The children could not help tasting
a little.

Creak! The door opened.
Out peeped an old woman,
smiling sweetly.
"Do come in, my dears,"
she said, beckoning.

But as soon as they stepped inside,
she locked the door. She was a
wicked witch!

"Now I've caught you!" she screeched.
"You, girl, can be my servant. But I've
got other plans for you, greedy boy!"

The witch locked Hansel inside an
empty chicken cage.

"You may be thin as a stick now,"
she said, cackling. "but I'll fatten
you up in no time."

Each day, the witch took handfuls of sweets to the cage. Although she peered in, she could not see Hansel clearly. She could not see very well at all.

"Poke out your finger, boy. I need to
know how fat you are growing."
Hansel did so.
"You're still too thin," she declared,
"but you'll be just right soon."

Gretel had a cunning idea.

"Hansel," she said, "when the witch asks for your finger, hold out this chicken bone." Hansel did just that.

"Grrr!!" the witch grumbled. "The boy's still too thin to gobble up!"

One day, the witch decided to eat both children anyway.

She made Gretel take wood to the oven.

Then she pointed at Hansel.

"I don't care if you are fat or thin.

You will be my dinner tonight!"

Hansel was terrified. How could

he escape?

Once the oven was glowing, the witch spoke to Gretel. She planned to eat her first.

"Girl," she said, "climb inside and tell me if the oven's hot enough."

Gretel was clever. She pretended
she didn't understand.

"I don't know how," Gretel wept.

"Should my head go in
first? Or my feet?"

"You stupid girl! Watch how I get in!"

the witch screeched.

She bent right over ...

... and Gretel pushed as hard as she could. The witch toppled straight into the oven. Gretel slammed the door shut. "That's the end of you, wicked witch," she shouted.

Gretel unlocked the cage and out
crawled Hansel.

They found a room full of stolen treasure.

"Let's take this home, Gretel," said Hansel. "Then we'll never be poor or hungry again."

Hansel and Gretel soon found
their way home.

Their father waved joyfully when he saw them. "I feared you were lost forever," he said.

From that day onwards, the family lived in great happiness.

About the story

Hansel and Gretel is a fairy tale from Germany. It was published by the Brothers Grimm in 1812. In the original story, the children are deliberately left in the woods by their stepmother because there is not enough food for them all. They find their way home by leaving a trail of pebbles. The children are soon taken into the woods again, and this time they can only leave a trail of breadcrumbs. The breadcrumbs are eaten by birds so the children get lost.

Be in the story!

Imagine you are the witch.

What will you say to tempt the children into your home?

Now imagine you are Hansel and Gretel's father. What will you say to your children when you see them again?

First published in 2014 by
Franklin Watts
338 Euston Road
London
NW1 3BH

Franklin Watts Australia
Level 17/207 Kent Street
Sydney
NSW 2000

A CIP catalogue record for this book is available
from the British Library.

The artwork for this story first appeared in
Leapfrog: Hansel and Gretel

ISBN 978 1 4451 2847 4 (hbk)
ISBN 978 1 4451 2848 1 (pbk)
ISBN 978 1 4451 2850 4 (library ebook)
ISBN 978 1 4451 2849 8 (ebook)

Series Editor: Jackie Hamley
Series Advisor: Catherine Glavina
Series Designer: Cathryn Gilbert

Printed in China

Franklin Watts is a divison of
Hachette Children's Books,
an Hachette UK company.
www.hachette.co.uk